Transforming Industry
Through Data Analytics

*Digital Disruption in Cities, Energy,
Manufacturing, Healthcare, and
Transportation*

Raghunath Nambiar

Beijing · Boston · Farnham · Sebastopol · Tokyo

Transforming Industry Through Data Analytics

by Raghunath Nambiar

Published by O'Reilly Media, Inc., 1005 Gravenstein Highway North, Sebastopol, CA 95472.

O'Reilly books may be purchased for educational, business, or sales promotional use. Online editions are also available for most titles (*http://oreilly.com/safari*). For more information, contact our corporate/institutional sales department: 800-998-9938 or *corporate@oreilly.com*.

Editors: Colleen Toporek and Shannon Cutt	**Interior Designer:** David Futato
Production Editor: Kristen Brown	**Cover Designer:** Karen Montgomery
Copyeditor: Octal Publishing, Inc.	**Illustrator:** Rebecca Demarest

September 2017:   First Edition

Revision History for the First Edition
2017-08-28:   First Release

978-1-491-99743-7

[LSI]

To my family, friends, and mentors, who keep challenging me to do new things.

Table of Contents

Preface

Since the dawn of time, humans have steadily improved every aspect of life by applying their intellect to the world around them. We call this practical application of knowledge "technology," and the history of the world is that of one technological advancement after another. Technology does not advance in a smooth continuous line. There are innovative leaps during which step-function changes occur, followed by long periods of improvement and refinement until the next innovation.

These leaps in technology are incredibly disruptive, providing both challenge and opportunity. Enterprises that recognize the challenge, adapt to the change, and take advantage of the opportunity are the ones that succeed and thrive; those that don't die off.

With the advent of computers, a new kind of technology was born: one based on the storage, retrieval and processing of data. This *information technology*, or *informatics*, dramatically changed the way we view and analyze the world around us. As a technology, informatics is also subject to the same innovative, step-function advances of all technologies, but with one important difference: the speed with which change occurs in informatics is significantly faster than with non-information technologies.

When we look back we view these leaps in technology and informatics as discreet points in time. In actual fact, there is a transition period during which the technology is developed and refined, and then applied to everyday life, bringing positive changes.

We are in the midst of one such transition now as the combination of ubiquitous low-cost computing power, an easily accessible globe-spanning network, and advanced data processing techniques initiates a digital transformation in which everything in the world—every person and every object—is producing data that can be harnessed to create capabilities unheard of just a short time ago.

But data production by itself is not useful. It is the collection, storage and, most important, analysis of the data that allows us to realize the incredible opportunity.

Join me as we look at what the foundations of digital transformation are and what their impact is on our lives, and, most important, how to harness the data through analytics to improve our cities, energy production, manufacturing, transportation, and healthcare.

Before we begin I owe thanks to a great many people who provided encouragement and support while I was engaged in this project. In particular, N.C. Ouseph, Meikel Poess, Paul Perez, Satinder Sethi, and Liz Centoni, who encouraged me to keep writing. Also, thanks to Shane Handy for doing an excellent job editing this book—without his help this would not have become a reality. And much appreciation is due to my colleagues for their help, advice, support, and friendship.

—*Raghunath Nambiar*
July 2017
San Jose, California

CHAPTER 1

Introduction

Everything is going digital. By the year 2020, seven billion people will have access to the internet, roughly half through a traditional wired connection, the other half wirelessly via mobile devices.

Similarly, current growth predictions put the number of devices connected to the internet by the year 2020 at 50 billion; by the year 2030 this number skyrockets to 500 billion (see Figure 1-1).

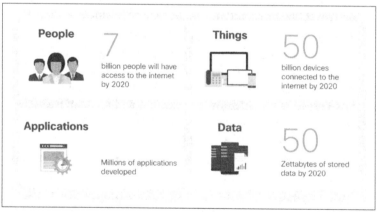

Figure 1-1. Pillars of digital transformation

In terms of data, by the year 2020, there will be 50 zettabytes of stored data. To give some perspective, that's equivalent to 50 billion one terabyte disk drives. What's more, by the year 2030, this number will increase by an order of magnitude.

These are impressive numbers by themselves, but it pales in comparison when you consider that when you connect something to the internet, it is not just connected to the network, *it is connected to everything else.*

Thus, we see an unprecedented opportunity as the number of connections explodes. The greatest opportunity exists where those connections are most dense, yet these are the areas where it is most difficult to make predictions. We humans have a tendency to overestimate what will happen in the next two years and underestimate what will happen in the next 10 years. This has never been truer than it is now as we approach this singularity of connections.

The rapid pace of technological change is often cited by senior executives as the biggest threat to their business. Consider that only 12 percent of the Fortune 500 companies from 1955 still exist today, and only 50 percent of current Fortune 500 companies are expected to still be in business just 10 years from now. Note that today's Fortune 500 companies represent more than two-thirds of the GDP in the United States.

Examples abound:

- Amazon put Borders bookstores out of business and all but destroyed the brick and mortar bookstore business.
- Netflix drove Blockbuster out of business and has its sights set on premium cable TV (Netflix's subscription revenue now exceeds that of HBO). It's worth noting that originally Netflix mailed DVDs to its customers, building its business through low-cost, convenience, a wide selection and an analytics-driven recommendation engine. That business is all but dead, having been replaced by Netflix's own streaming service.
- Uber and other ride-hailing services have transformed the taxi industry.
- Airbnb is threatening the hotel business, and the list goes on.

It's called *creative destruction*, and it's an extinction event for companies that are unwilling or unable to adapt. Analytics capabilities have become the differentiator. Analyzing data to understand the business and how to guide it through treacherous technology revolutions is the difference between a growing, thriving company and extinction.

To understand how to proceed let's first look at the specific challenges we face as we work to tame the deluge of data being generated, changing it from meaningless bits into actionable insight. Next, we'll review the four different types of analysis, what they are, how they're used, and what kind of analytical system is required to enable them. Lastly, we'll look at how the incredible explosion of connections, in the form of devices and people, and how our ability to make use of the data they generate, will affect our cities, the energy sector, the manufacturing industry, transportation, and, arguably the most important, health care.

CHAPTER 2

Digital Transformation

The amount of data being created is simply exploding. As we move deeper into the era of digital transformation, there are many more sources of data of many different types. The majority of the data—more than 90 percent—is unstructured (e.g, email, text documents, images, audio, and video). These data types are a poor fit for relational databases and traditional storage methods. There is tremendous value in the data, but taking advantage of all of it for business insight is challenging at both the technical and semantic level.

Technical Challenges

From a technical perspective, to make use of the data, we must collect, transfer, store, and process it. The sheer volume of data presents significant challenges. Unprocessed data is useless, so compute requirements are growing in direct response to the data growth. Thus, more powerful servers (or, as it turns out, more servers working in parallel) are needed.

New data management software frameworks have been developed (Hadoop, NoSQL) that can process massive amounts of data in parallel across a large cluster of servers. These frameworks have storage services built in; for example, replication, self-healing, rebalancing, and scaling out by adding servers. Traditional systems have to rely on underlying storage arrays to provide these services. Tighter integration of storage services with the data management layer provides a lot of flexibility. For example, you can increase or decrease the number or replicas, tune the timing to start healing (in case of a disk or server failure) and even tune the level of consistency based on the application's requirements.

From the infrastructure perspective, highly optimized platforms have been developed, made up of clusters of servers with dense internal storage interconnected using a high-speed network. These are designed to scale out and have sophisticated management and administration capabilities significantly easing the burden of managing hundreds or thousands of servers.

Looking ahead, the amount of data being generated at the edge of the network by connected devices is growing dramatically. This poses new challenges and introduces the concept of the edge- or local-context and enterprise- (data center/cloud) or global-context. In Chapter 3, we will discuss edge-to-enterprise analytics in detail.

As the increasing reliance on information technology becomes more pervasive, the underlying technologies (compute, storage, and network at the edge and enterprise) will improve in line with Moore's Law, Amdahl's Law and their derivatives, and my own Nambiar's Law. The technologies available will become universal, so analytics capabilities (i.e., how well you know your business, your customers, and your partners—and how quickly you understand them) will become the core of your business. In other words, you will become data-driven—and by extension, analytics-driven.

Data Challenges

It is a nontrivial exercise to turn data into information, in large part because of what's become known as the *five "V's" of big data*: volume, variety, velocity, veracity, and value, as illustrated in Figure 2-1.

Let's look at each of these in a bit more detail.

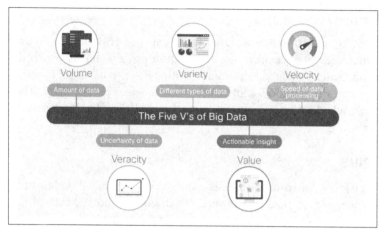

Figure 2-1. The five V's of big data

Volume

The *volume* of data has grown so much that traditional relational database management software running on monolithic servers is incapable of processing it.

Variety

The *variety* of data has increased. Structured data has been the norm, but is no longer. Unstructured data requires new approaches to collect, store, and process it into something useful.

Our ability to process unstructured data changes the way we approach data analysis and application development. Previously, you would define your data structures and build an application to operate on the data. The lifetime of these kinds of applications was often measured in years.

Now, data is collected in its original fidelity and explored for meaningful patterns. Applications are built to take advantage of these patterns, and then rebuilt when new patterns emerge. The lifetime of the applications is much shorter: months to days.

Velocity

Velocity is the measure of how fast the data is coming in. It has to be processed, often in real time, and stored in huge volume.

Veracity

Veracity of data refers to how much you can trust it. Traditional structured data goes through a validation process during which it's cleaned up, validated, and joined with related data. This requires that you already know a lot about the data before processing it. This approach does not work with unstructured data (as discussed in "variety").

Value

Deriving value from the data is non-trivial, especially in light of the challenges presented by the other V's discussed above. Much of the progress made in compute, storage, and networking, and in distributed data processing frameworks is aimed at addressing these challenges with the goal of converting data into actionable insight.

Three "I's" of Big Data

Another way to look at the data challenge is with the *three "I's" of big data* (see Figure 2-2): investment, innovation, and improvisation. Investment in collecting, analyzing, and using data is mandatory if your enterprise wants to avoid extinction, as previously discussed. Innovation is what you're able to do, making use of previously unexplored data to provide new products and new services, and create better customer experiences. Improvisation is the ability to explore the data, find new meaning, and turn it into actionable insight in a continuous cycle.

Realizing that the data itself is as important as how it can be processed, one way to approach understanding what is happening now and what will happen in the future is to look at the different ways in which we can process and analyze the data.

In the next section, we discuss the four different types of analysis, what they are and how they're used, ranging from the simplest to the most sophisticated. We then review the different kinds of analytical systems that we can implement to produce the required analyses.

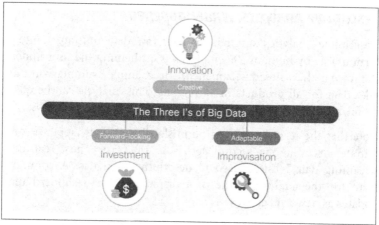

Figure 2-2. The three I's of big data

Types of Analytics

Let's take a look at the different kinds of analysis that are possible as well as the different types of systems that we can use to produce the analyses.

There are four types of analyses, ranging from relatively basic descriptions of what has happened to very sophisticated guidance on what actions to take (see Figure 2-3). Let's look more closely at them.

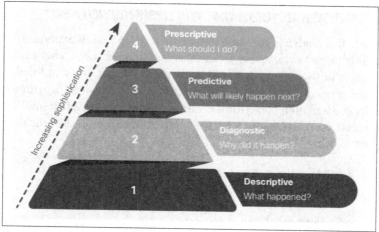

Figure 2-3. Types of analysis

Descriptive Analytics: *What Happened?*

Descriptive analytics summarizes past raw data putting it into a form usable by humans. Its emphasis is on helping the user understand what has already happened; for example, summarizing all sales data for all products in all regions. This analysis can be quite useful, allowing the user to view the data in many different ways.

Note that the term "past" can be misleading. What happened one minute, or even one second ago is in the past. Thus, real-time streaming data is often used in descriptive analytics. A common form for the analysis is the data displayed in a dashboard that updates as new data arrives.

Diagnostic Analytics: *Why Did It Happen?*

Diagnostic analytics are used for root-cause analysis to understand why something happened. For example: why sales were low in a particular region last month (the weather); or why sales for a particular product were low (high returns due to quality issues, or competitor pricing); or why a product is out of stock (supply chain issues or an unexpected spike in demand).

Knowing what happened from descriptive analytics and why it happened from diagnostic analytics enables management to make informed decisions about what course of action to take.

Predictive Analytics: *What Will Likely Happen Next?*

Predictive analytics goes one step further. By analyzing patterns and trends in past data, analysts can make predictions about what could happen in the future, using this information to set goals and make plans. Predictive analytics applies a variety of statistical algorithms to past data, often correlating it with past outcomes in an attempt to forecast what will happen next. Examples of common uses include the following:

- What-if analysis
- Data mining
- Root cause analysis
- Forecasting
- Monte Carlo simulation

Prescriptive Analytics: *What Should I Do?*

Prescriptive analytics is the next logical step after predictive analysis. Prescriptive analytics is a combination of data, mathematical models and various business rules that are used to run simulations—often called scenario analysis—using various sets of assumptions.

By varying the assumptions and applying a variety of optimization techniques prescriptive analysis suggests what actions are likely to maximize a given business outcome. In other words, prescriptive analysis explores several possible actions helping to identify what actions produce the best result.

Types of Analytical Systems

The previous section described the different types of analysis, but not the kinds of systems needed to produce them. There are many different types of analytical systems available for use and which one you use is based largely on the kind of data with which you're working. These analytical systems have overlaps and in many cases coexist and complement one another. They are by no means plug-and-play; rather, they require complex data-level and process-level integrations. Figure 2-4 presents the different types of systems.

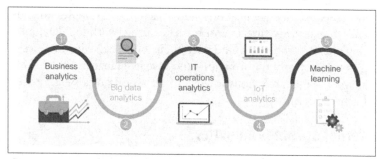

Figure 2-4. Types of analytical systems

Business Analytics

Business analytics brings together data from disparate sources to provide a more complete picture of what has happened or is happening now in the business.

Traditional data warehousing and business intelligence tools fall into this category. They excel when the data is structured and the relationships between the data are well understood.

Big Data Analytics

Big data analytics has emerged in the past decade and is characterized by the 5 V's described in the previous section—very large volumes of data from many different data sources of differing data types, often moving very quickly. These systems can handle very large volumes of data (terabytes to petabytes) and excel at processing unstructured data. It makes possible things that traditional data warehousing and business intelligence (BI) systems are incapable of doing.

Examples include search engine companies indexing web pages; credit card processors detecting fraud; online advertisers targeting ads to specific demographics; and sentiment analysis of news and social media to understand customer perception of the business.

IT Operations Analytics

Information technology operations analytics are a specialized subset of big data analytics. They are specifically designed to analyze log data generated by applications and machines. Examples include identifying security threats and breaches in network log data; analyzing clickstream data to understand customer behavior on a website; or a security information and event management (SIEM) system, a 360-degree, holistic view of all aspects of an enterprise's information security.

Internet of Things Analytics

Earlier, we discussed the explosion of data at the edge of the network caused by the increase in the number of connected devices. This Internet of Things (IoT) requires new analytical tools. IoT analytics falls into two main categories. The first is performing analysis at the edge of the network, at or near the devices generating the data. This is necessary when the response from the analysis is required quickly; for example, adjusting equipment to operate more efficiently, or shutting down a tool as a protective measure; and when it is impractical to send the data back to the enterprise datacenter, either because there is too much data, or the available bandwidth is limited.

The second category of analysis is performed at the enterprise-level, typically in the enterprise datacenter, on all of the data from all devices in aggregate. By looking at all data from all devices, analysts and engineers create a more complete picture and gain a deeper understanding of what is happening. When it comes to then using that data for model building, it's simple: more data equals better models. These models are pushed to the edge making the analytics at the edge more efficient.

Examples include creating new models to be used in edge analysis; analyzing the output of all sensors or data in aggregate in order to optimize the edge device; and defining parameters to be used in proactive or predictive maintenance. We will discuss this in detail in Chapter 3.

Machine Learning

Only very recently has machine learning come to the fore as a practical analytical tool. This is because of recent developments in both specialized hardware and new software algorithms. The hardware enables the machine learning system to operate fast enough to be useful (e.g, more cores, GPUs, FPGAs). The software techniques have dramatically improved the speed with which the systems can be taught (e.g., CUDA, TensorFlow).

Machine learning and its impact on analytical systems is beyond the scope of this book, but there is a key point to keep in mind as the technology progresses and becomes more accessible: traditional, statistics-based analysis requires a human expert to define and then test the relationship between cause and effect.

Machine learning works in the opposite direction. It begins with the effect and teaches the system to automatically find what factors contribute to the outcome. The factors involved might be very complex, far more so than a human can handle, including hundreds of factors and their interactions with one another. Done correctly, we can create highly accurate predictive models. Even more, these models can automatically adjust over time as new data comes in creating an increasingly refined, ever-improving model.

CHAPTER 3

Edge-to-Enterprise Analytics

The technical challenges brought on by the advent of the IoT require new system architectures in order to capture and process the data. The first challenge is capturing all of the data from the edge; in other words, gathering information from the IoT and devices and transferring it to the enterprise datacenter. When you consider there are potentially millions of devices involved, it quickly becomes apparent that making direct connections from the edge devices to the enterprise datacenter is not a workable solution.

Additionally, depending on the use case, the number of edge devices can change, up or down, over time as new devices come online and others are retired. Even devices that will persist in sending data can drop off the network and come back online later. To address this, a transfer layer (commonly called an IoT gateway) is inserted between the edge devices and the enterprise datacenter, as depicted in Figure 3-1.

Figure 3-1 is, admittedly, a very simple diagram, but it illustrates the point. The message brokers between the edge and the enterprise act as a temporary holding area. Edge devices transfer data to the brokers as they generate it, and the enterprise consumes it from the brokers. The enterprise communicates only with the brokers. Each edge device needs to know only the address of the broker. The message broker needs to be highly available, fault-tolerant, resilient, and capable of handling large volumes of data (Apache Kafka comes to mind).

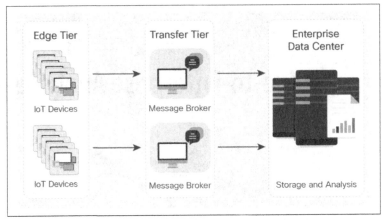

Figure 3-1. Layers from edge to enterprise

In addition to dealing with the variability in the number of IoT devices, this approach has other benefits. It creates a buffer between the devices generating the data and the enterprise. Thus, if the enterprise systems go offline for scheduled maintenance, the brokers continue to accept data from the edge devices, queueing it up for when the enterprise systems come back online.

This also deals with issues related to geography. for cases in which devices are spread over great distances or even all over the world, many brokers can be used, with the IoT devices communicating with whatever broker is closest (and thus has the lowest latency).

Another technical challenge is dealing with cases in which a fast response is required by the device generating the data. There often is not time to ship the data over the network to the enterprise datacenter, analyze it, formulate a response and send it back.

In this case, the analysis and response must occur closer to where the data is being generated. In Figure 3-2, IoT devices send data to an edge node (or an IoT gateway system) where analysis and response occur in real time. The edge node then sends the data to the enterprise datacenter. Here, it is aggregated with all of the data from every device and analyzed for use in understanding the business, and in the creation, modification or refinement of the analysis to be performed by the edge node.

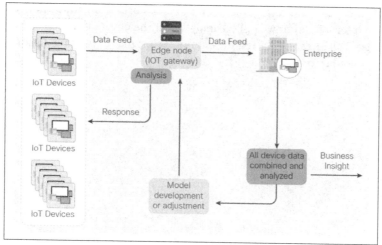

Figure 3-2. Edge-to-enterprise analytics

The edge node is close to the edge devices such that limited bandwidth or network latency do not affect the timely arrival of the data and receipt of any response. The edge node can be a server dedicated for this purpose, or even embedded in the network router. The latter is a particularly elegant solution because that device is needed anyway to route the network traffic.

Finally, the edge node can be programmed to first filter[1] the data before sending it to the enterprise datacenter (note that this will be done via a message broker—not shown in the diagram for clarity's sake). This addresses the issue for which it is impractical to send everything due to the sheer volume of data involved as well as cases for which there is a lot of "noise" in the data, which will just be deleted after it reaches the enterprise data center.

In the enterprise, typically at the enterprise data center, all of the data from all the edge devices is combined to create a global context. This context is used for real-time response on the macro scale, as well as traditional historical analysis. It is also used to build and refine the analyses that are implemented at the edge.

---

1 Filtering is just another kind of analysis.

We now turn our attention to how the explosion in connections to the internet and how applied analytics, at the edge and in the enterprise, will affect our cities, the energy sector, manufacturing, health-care, and transportation.

CHAPTER 4

Smart Cities

Urban populations are rising. In 2014, 54 percent of the world's population lived in cities. According to the United Nations, this number is projected to increase to 66 percent by 2050. In 1990, there were 10 megacities (defined as a city with a population of more than 10 million). This number almost tripled over the next 30 years; in 2014, there were 28 megacities. The UN estimates there will be 41 megacities by 2030.

Cities currently consume 75% of the world's resources and generate 80% of the greenhouse gases. Given the projected continued urbanization of the planet, we can expect these numbers to increase. It's clear that we need better methods for managing cities. The issues we see today will only be amplified as the population grows.

Throughout history, humans have applied technological advances to improve cities. Skyscrapers, mass transit, wastewater treatment, and traffic lights are all examples of the use of technology to solve an urban living problem. We are at a turning point in the evolution of the city for which the use of information and communication technology in general, and the IoT in particular, can be used in a practical way to address a wide variety of issues facing today's cities—in some cases, dramatically transforming the city in the process.

Specifically, technology exists today or is on the horizon to improve the following areas:

- Energy efficiency
- Traffic management

- Parking
- Environmental monitoring
- Structural monitoring
- Waste management
- Safety
- Crowd control

Environmental Monitoring

Environmental monitoring involves making use of sensors installed on devices along with location-based sensors to track conditions related to the environment in order to respond directly to an issue or collect data to be analyzed.

Sensors that track water usage can identify both macro- and micro-issues. Total water usage by building can be tracked and analyzed for outliers, allowing the city management to focus on high-value improvement areas. Similarly, water flow sensors make identifying and finding leaks much faster, reducing, and in some cases eliminating, waste (sensor-enabled valves can automatically close when leaks are detected). In addition, sensors on the water meters automate the process for collecting the data for usage and billing.

In parks and public areas, ground sensors monitor the moisture content of the soil to be used to more efficiently and automatically manage the water-delivery systems (sprinklers, drip-feed, and so on). As the sensors grow in sophistication, other nutrients can also be supplied automatically, providing specific amounts of fertilizer and food to the plants.

In a similar vein, sensors can automatically sample the air, collecting data such as temperature, barometric pressure, carbon dioxide, carbon monoxide, light levels, and moisture content. The only limiting factor with respect to what we can monitor is the sophistication of the sensor itself. Moisture content is particularly interesting because it's not what comes to mind when considering air quality, but it has interesting follow-on uses including identifying where to plant trees that ultimately reduce the overall temperature and lower cooling costs.

Sensor packages deployed throughout the city provide a wealth of data for analysis to aid in making data-driven decisions.

Energy Efficiency

We will discuss the transformation in the energy sector in more detail later on. As it pertains to cities, buildings and streetlights are the obvious targets to improve energy usage. Advances in technology allow for streetlights that use bulbs requiring much less energy and that emit dramatically less "light pollution." These improvements can be extended further when coupled with sensors enabling the streetlight to adjust its brightness. In addition, as solar power and battery technologies advance, the streetlights themselves can be disconnected from the electric grid, or even net providers of electricity, particularly during the longer days of the summer months.

Finally, the sheer number of streetlights and their distribution throughout the city make them prime candidates to house the aforementioned sensor packages (the city of Chicago is already doing this). These sensors are not limited to just the environment: audio, and even video, can be added, which makes for some interesting capabilities.

Buildings represent a large portion of the resource consumption of cities. The American Council for an Energy Efficient Economy (ACEEE) estimates that even a modest improvement in only 35 percent of the commercial buildings in the United States alone would save up to $60 billion annually.

An integrated building energy management system monitors heating, cooling, and electricity consumption optimizing usage in real time while also identifying problems and issuing appropriate responses. Predictive maintenance capabilities like those discussed in the manufacturing section will reduce cost and improve overall equipment efficiency.

These systems implement advanced control strategies such as the following:

- Multispeed fans and demand control ventilation technologies for heating and cooling
- Smart windows that lighten and darken the windows to let in or keep out sunlight

- Integrated heating, ventilation, and air conditioning (HVAC) decisions with the smart windows to choose the most efficient use of the energy
- Sensors on all electricity-using devices, adjusting their use based on demand, in particular, reducing usage automatically during peak times. For example, lowering light levels and turning off nonmandatory displays.

In addition to these specific improvements, there is the larger general benefit of having the data to analyze to understand usage and make decisions based on that data. A next step is integrating the energy management systems of each building with all the others, thus enabling a city-wide view of both usage and response to demand.

Traffic Management

Traffic management in cities is on the cusp of a major transformation. Cities around the world are already implementing advanced technologies to improve transportation to, from, and within cities.

Sensor-enabled public transportation vehicles can provide real-time status on location and expected arrival times. They also can adjust to demand, changing their stops, routes and frequency as needed.

Video analytics is progressing to a point that new capabilities are coming online. Real-time license-plate reading, originally used to enforce stoplight and toll-road laws, is now commonplace. This kind of surveillance-based video analytics can be expanded to include many other traffic laws, especially speeding.

The same systems can identify congestion and post alerts to commuters, and also integrate with the traffic-light system to improve traffic flow. This can then be integrated with emergency vehicles to aid first responders in getting to their destination as quickly as possible.

No discussion of traffic management is complete without considering the impact of autonomous vehicles. Real-world tests of self-driving vehicles are underway with estimates that they'll be commonplace ranging from 5 to 20 years from now.

The transformative nature of this technology cannot be overstated. We have already seen a sea change in private transportation via crowd sourcing with companies like Scoop (for carpooling) and Uber and Lyft (for taxi services). These companies use connected and mobile technologies to change how we travel to, from, and within the city; but it is easy to see self-driving, electric cars take this one step further, either individually-owned private cars, or fleets of cars owned by a new kind of transportation business. Fleets of self-driving cars, shuttles, and buses owned and run by the city government will replace the current public transportation system and potentially extend it much further.

The benefits are profound. All-electric, autonomous vehicles have zero emissions to reduce pollution, are safer, and reduce congestion because they require fewer vehicles overall and can coordinate their activities. Package delivery services will also change. There is an opportunity to dramatically improve delivery services, a real problem on crowded city streets, particularly in conjunction with delivery drones.

It is not unreasonable to envision a time when autonomous vehicles will be mandatory in the city or parts of the city, and the use of human-controlled vehicles will be banned.

Parking

Adding sensor technology to parking lots and structures and making this information available to mobile-connected drivers is more efficient and reduces traffic (no more driving in circles looking for a spot). We already see this in a primitive fashion at some parking structures where the number of open parking spots by floor is displayed at the entrance.

Here is another case for which autonomous vehicles will have a dramatic impact, both near- and far-reaching. Autonomous vehicles don't need to park at their destination. If they're part of a shared usage scenario, they don't need to park at all (only a temporary pick-up and drop-off). If they're privately owned, they don't need to park nearby. They simply can drop off their owner and then be directed to a parking area in a less congested part of the city.

A far-reaching consequence is the change in land use and architecture. When autonomous vehicles are ubiquitous, city buildings will not need parking structures, instead they can use the space more productively, but will need to provide mechanisms for dropping off and picking up passengers on a much larger scale than is currently needed. Further, valuable land will not need to be used for parking structures. This space can be put to better use for other buildings, parks, or open space.

The same applies to airports, stadiums, or other event venues. Huge swaths of land are currently used to park cars that sit there for hours and days. This kind of parking, located near the destination, will be extinct in the future.

Safety

As cities grow in size and complexity, keeping citizens safe becomes more challenging. In recent times, there has been an explosion in the number of surveillance cameras installed worldwide. Beyond the obvious benefit of helping law enforcement solve crimes and apprehend criminals, many studies have shown that video surveillance acts as a deterrent reducing crime by its mere presence. Video analytics technology is advancing rapidly, and with new software algorithms and powerful processors, new capabilities are becoming available.

Facial recognition is probably the most widely talked about safety-related technology and is beginning to see practical applications in real-world use, particular in airports. But the technology is more far-reaching than identification. Video analytics will be able to identify suspect behavior. For example, analysis shows it takes a certain amount of time to find your car in the parking lot, and there is a specific pattern to how people move from the entrance to their car. Video analytics can identify when someone does not match this profile and can alert security in real time.

Many cities are investing in extensive networks of surveillance cameras. Some of the challenges facing human operators is finding someone or something (e.g., a car) that matches a description and then having found them tracking them through the various camera feeds. This needs to be done both historically, after the fact, as part of an investigation, and in real time, as events unfold.

Video analytics is advancing to the point where the human operators will be able to input a description—for example, male, about six feet tall, wearing a green shirt—and in real time find all people matching that description. After an identification is made, the system will be able to track that person through the various surveillance camera feeds, also in real time.

After the fact, the human operators could institute a search with the same description, specifying the time and geolocation parameters and the system would present them with all people found matching that description. The system can then "follow" that person forward through time.

These examples of identifying suspect behavior, finding someone matching a description and tracking something through the system are easier than facial recognition in some ways and much more difficult in others. The sheer amount of data that must be transferred across the network and processed is mind-boggling and simply wasn't possible prior to recent advances in network and processor technology.

These systems are not limited to government agencies. Private surveillance systems can identify suspect behavior and alert security, but they also can integrate directly with police and issue an alert based on the suspected behavior. An example would be detection of a firearm. Another is detecting a fire and notifying the fire department.

These are very dramatic uses of video analytics, but more mundane uses are potentially more meaningful. Video surveillance systems at intersections can be used to identify people in a crosswalk and delay the changing of the traffic light to green. The same systems can identify lost children in stores, airports, train stations, or any public area.

Earlier, we discussed sensor packages installed on streetlights. Audio sensors as part of that package can be used to detect a gunshot, triangulate its location, and direct police to the area. This is already being done using custom hardware. What makes it interesting is when the audio sensors are everywhere. It's not difficult to envision a time when someone, anywhere in the city, can call for help (literally, "Help, police!") and have the call detected, routed, and responded to automatically.

Crowd Control

Continuing with video analytics, a basic capability in the future is counting the number of people entering and leaving a building or area. This can be used to automatically detect violations of the fire code and alert the appropriate personnel (management or security). It can also be used to help the fire department understand how many people are still in the building, both from the count and by switching the system to an emergency mode that is specifically designed to interact with emergency services personnel.

There is another aspect to consider. It will be possible to automatically identify people entering a building and determining if certain individuals are authorized to be there. This can be done in a very sophisticated way through the use of facial recognition. A simpler method is to interact with their smartphones. In this way, the smartphone replaces the badges most companies use.

The Internet of Everything

We call it the Internet of Things, referring to sensor-enabled devices connected to the internet, but it's really the Internet of Everything. Every "thing" in the world, literally everything, can be connected to the internet and interact with the environment. By way of closing out this section, let's consider a few miscellaneous things that are not obvious candidates for the IoT.

First, trash cans: sensors installed on waste receptacles detect when the container is full and communicate that information to a central station. This data is used to make more efficient use of the trucks and personnel that collect the trash, skipping receptacles that aren't full and prioritizing those that are, optimizing the route in the process. It might seem far-fetched but it's already being done.

Secondly, consider the structural monitoring of bridges. Sensors installed on bridges collect data on the load and the environment (wind, especially) identifying issues before they become a catastrophe. The data is also analyzed and used to better understand how the structure reacts to different combinations of load and weather, ultimately helping to build better bridges. The same can be done for buildings, particularly skyscrapers, especially those in earthquake zones.

Finally, let's address a bane of modern life: pot holes. Street maintenance is expensive and ripe for optimization. If the city's maintenance services can identify cracks in the street, they can respond before the cracks become expensive-to-repair holes. Cameras on the underside of vehicles can use video analytics to identify cracks and transmit the data back to a central station. This is actually a much easier video analytics task than those already discussed. But, what vehicles? Post office delivery vans are one choice. They're government owned and they go everywhere, but ultimately, every single autonomous vehicle can be used for this purpose, given that the hardware needed is already installed.

CHAPTER 5

Transforming the Energy Sector

Data analysis is transforming the energy sector in enormously influential ways. We discuss some of these in this section.

Smart Grid

The energy sector has been undergoing a transformation for some time now into what is commonly referred to as the *smart grid*. The smart grid is a modernization of the electrical grid from a monolithic system characterized by the one-way flow of both power and information to a more distributed system in which electricity is produced and consumed throughout the grid, including all the way out at the very edges, and information about power production and consumption flows in both directions.

Electricity is unusual in that there is no real "inventory" of stored electricity that consumers draw upon, with the producers then refilling the inventory supply. Instead, the amount of electricity consumed must match the amount produced. Blackouts and brownouts occur when the demand exceeds the grid's ability to supply the amount of power needed at that time.

Thus, data about the demand for power and the supply of power is incredibly useful in making the electrical grid more efficient. One of the first steps in the evolution of the smart grid was intelligent metering whereby the amount of power being consumed at each endpoint is automatically gathered in real time or near real time and transmitted back to the producer. Previously, meters were manually read on a very infrequent basis (e.g., monthly) and provided almost no information on how and when the power was being used.

This was just the first step. The same data can be sent to the consumer, enabling their own analysis; and the smart meters can also monitor the quality of the power, and provide real-time notification of outages.

One way the utilities help deal with peak demand is through *demand–response* actions wherein the price of electricity is raised during peak times as an incentive to consumers to reduce their usage. Historically, this has been driven by edge and enterprise-level analytics to understand peak times and communicate the price changes to consumers, who then can adjust their usage as they are able.

With the advent of smart meters, and keeping in mind our earlier discussion of smart cities, this demand–response loop can be automated to a large extent. For example, the utility company sends signals that there is an increase in demand, and the smart buildings and smart homes respond by lowering their usage. The responses can range from the simple—turning off the air-conditioning and lowering the light levels—to the sophisticated—darkening windows on the sun-facing side of the structure, increasing light levels and lowering the air conditioning, while on the opposite side, lightening the windows, turning off the air conditioning and increasing the ventilation.

Let's stop for a moment and examine the data and analytics in use here. This is important for what comes next. Previously, the utilities would adjust the supply up and down to the best of their ability in order to meet demand. The initial application of demand–response was very simple: raise prices for everyone during peak times, and lower prices when demand is low.

With data from smart meters, both the producers and consumers can make decisions. Sophisticated analytics show producers how much electricity is being used, who is using it and when. This allows them to create targeted demand-response signals that are optimized to match the supply with the demand.

From the consumer's perspective, data from smart meters enables detailed analyses on their energy usage. For a manufacturer, this might mean shifting certain production processes to a different shift to take advantage of lower energy costs. At home, consumers can make similar decisions, running the washer, dryer, and dishwasher at night (and running them staggered instead of all at once).

Furthermore, with the advent of the IoT and two-way communication via the smart grid, a consumer can prep the washer, dryer, and dishwasher, and then define parameters for when they should run; or, looking further ahead, specify when to charge their electric car, something that will have a much greater impact as electric vehicles beome the norm. These parameters are based on demand-response signals from the utilities. Applying analytics to the data from all homes and buildings results in an intelligent matching of demand to supply and a very efficient electric grid.

Renewable Energy Sources

Occurring in tandem with the evolution of the smart grid is the mainstream acceptance of newer power generation technologies in the form of renewable sources like wind and solar. Solar energy, in particular, has been on an exponential growth curve from 2007 to 2017, consistently exceeding all estimates.

Beyond the obvious environmental benefits of solar power, the dramatic increase in the number of utility-scale solar power installations is due to the equally dramatic reduction in cost. In 2014, solar power cost $0.05/kilowatt hour (kWh). Two years later, the price had dropped to $0.04/kWh. Now, in 2017, prices have dropped further to $0.03/kWh. By contrast, the average global price of coal is $0.06/kWh.

It's important to remember that solar photovoltaics is not a fuel. It is a technology, and as such is subject to improvements through innovation that are not possible with the chemical reactions from burning fossil fuels.

Projections show the amount of power generated from solar power continuing to increase until it overtakes all other sources. It is not a question of if but when this will happen. Thus far, all projections have been woefully conservative.

Solar and wind power generation is variable. The amount of power produced varies with the time of day, the weather, and the time of year (days are shorter in winter). This presents a challenge with tremendous potential for analytics, given the need to match the supply of electricity to the demand.

Another factor is location. Wind turbines need to be placed in windy areas and the power transmitted to where it is needed. The same is true to a lesser extent for solar, though the relative abundance of sunlight (compared to wind) makes this less of an issue. Integrated analytics capabilities have tremendous potential to improve the performance of renewable energy systems through proactive and predictive maintenance, particularly for wind turbines (due to the greater number of moving parts).

In both cases, there is a clear transition being made from a small number of large, centralized power generation facilities to many smaller geographically distributed facilities. In addition, solar power can be installed for individual use on a structure-by-structure basis.

Distribution and Storage

The transition from centralized to distributed power generation requires even more data and analytics to coordinate energy production and distribution to meet demand, particularly with the variable nature of the energy production from wind and solar.

An IoT-enabled smart grid can optimize supply with demand using the industry's standard supply-side techniques and adjusting the demand side based on available supply. With solar energy making up a larger percentage of the total, some interesting things can happen. We usually think about delaying activities until night time when demand for energy is lower, but with solar power, supply is higher during the day and therefore we could see demand–response shifting to daytime.

Other possibilities are grid-aware charging systems for the increasing number of electric vehicles. Dynamically making even small changes in charging rates for electric car batteries can a have dramatic smoothing effect on power consumption.

With increasing numbers of solar arrays being installed on individual homes and buildings, all of which are producing electricity, new factors enter the equation. These installations use electricity where it's produced, eliminating the need (and costs) for transmission and distribution. But they also can produce more electricity than they need. This power can be fed back to the grid and made available to other consumers.

Individually, the amount of power is small, but collectively it can be quite large, complicating the demand/supply/distribution problem and making the need for smart systems capable of managing the coordination all the more apparent.

The demand/supply match problem can be mitigated by storing energy. Recent advances in technology have made battery storage, if not entirely economical, at least viable. In 2017, the California Public Utilities Commission installed Tesla batteries at one substation creating 80 megawatt hours (MWh) of storage (capable of powering 15,000 homes for four hours).

Most technological improvements in batteries have been inspired by electric cars, in which high-density and low-weight are key factors. For grid storage, low-density and low-cost are important. As the amount of solar power in use worldwide increases the need to store energy at grid-scale will increase and drive innovation in battery-based grid storage.

The combination of a decentralized smart grid, low-cost solar power, and battery grid storage give rise to the possibility of Solar Power as a Service business models, wherein private companies create local solar farms, connect it to the grid and sell power to the community.

CHAPTER 6

Transforming Manufacturing

Manufacturing has been evolving in leaps and bounds, and data has transformed this industry, as well.

Industry 4.0

The history of manufacturing is one of a continual quest for higher quality, greater efficiency, and lower cost. Improvements in these areas come as both step-function increases and incremental improvements (see Figure 6-1). The first dramatic increase came at the end of the eighteenth century with first the widespread use of water and then later steam power, enabling the creation of the first truly mechanical production facilities. This Age of Steam, a key enabler of the Industrial Revolution, would hold sway for more than a hundred years.

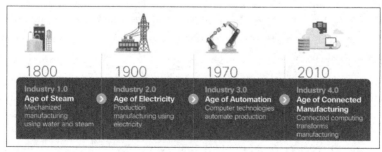

Figure 6-1. History of manufacturing

In the early twentieth century, improvements in the reliable generation and distribution of electricity along with advances in the design of electric motors heralded the death of steam giving birth to the Age of Electricity. This in turn was supplanted in the 1970s by revolutions in electronics and computers, which helped to automate much of the manufacturing process in the Age of Automation.

Each of these paradigm shifts was followed by a period of refinement during which the new manufacturing methods are improved over time (though the astute reader will have noticed the length of time between each new paradigm is reducing).

We are now on the cusp of the next dramatic change, the Age of Connected Manufacturing. Connected Manufacturing refers to the interconnection, to a common communications framework, of equipment, devices, people, products, and processes; everything involved in manufacturing connected in such a way that it can communicate with everything else. This is very different from the past, in which highly specific communication protocols were used for individual peer-to-peer connections.

Predictive Maintenance

By way of example, let's examine a high-value use case: predictive maintenance. Manufacturing equipment needs to be maintained in order to maximize uptime and minimize unplanned downtime. The latter is especially problematic because equipment that fails unexpectedly affects the production line both upstream and downstream. It can also ruin good product in the process. This is especially painful toward the end of the production process when a lot of value has been added to the product (in other words, it's expensive) and scrapping it so late in the production cycle can affect customer on-time delivery (put another way, customers are not happy when the product they need is late).

Manufacturing management puts a lot of time and effort into scheduling maintenance on all production equipment in order to avoid these negative outcomes as well as to keep the equipment running well and ensure high-quality products are being produced. Conventional approaches to equipment maintenance establish a schedule for inspecting and maintaining all the components of all the equipment. This schedule is fixed and is based on the mean time before failure data for each of the components.

This is a reasonable approach to the problem, but it's suboptimal in several ways:

- Scheduled maintenance replaces components that might not need to be replaced yet.
- Scheduled maintenance misses those cases in which the component fails before the next maintenance cycle.
- Manually inspecting equipment is time-consuming, expensive, and subject to human error.

And here is where edge and enterprise analytics really shine in a connected manufacturing environment. By making use of sensors on the equipment and connecting them to the network infrastructure they can push performance and diagnostic data to the connected manufacturing systems.

At the edge—the equipment itself—analytics can be run identifying conditions that raise alerts indicating maintenance is required. In extreme cases, the tool can be shut down immediately, stopping processing and protecting the product.

These analytics are using predictive models that are created via enterprise analytics. All of the data from similar tools are aggregated in the enterprise datacenter and analyzed. Predictive models are generated and tested using past data and then pushed out to the edge where they are applied on the production line.

This describes only a single factory. Taking it one step further, in a multifactory environment, all of the data from similar tools in all of the company's factories can be aggregated at a true enterprise level and analyzed in total. This allows the data, knowledge, and learning from every tool in every factory to inform the model creation and decision-making process. It also enables global views of the equipment that management can use to initiate discussions with vendors about improvements to the processing equipment.

Taking it one step further, the data from an individual tool can be sent to the equipment vendor where it is joined with the data from every other tool from every factory in the world. This is a powerful mechanism for the equipment maker to take advantage of the collective knowledge of the global community to improve its manufacturing equipment.

Another possibility is the equipment data can be sent to a third-party service that specializes in creating predictive models. As a business model, this possibility has a lot of advantages. It allows the manufacturer to outsource a difficult task with a high skill requirement while simultaneously allowing highly specialized technical experts to apply their know-how in a way that can improve the manufacturing process for all of their customers all over the world.

Further, the concept of proactive maintenance does not stop at the factory walls. New revenue streams can be created by providing a predictive maintenance service for the company's products at customer sites. With connected infrastructure as an enabler, imagine a home appliance manufacturer, or an automobile manufacturer, providing a predictive maintenance service to their customers. This capability can be designed right into the product itself.

Finally, the concept of a manufacturer being done with a product after it ships out the door is dying. Increasingly, manufacturers are extending their relationships with customers beyond the factory walls. By using their smart, connected factories to produce smart, connected products, manufacturers can engage with the customer directly through targeted feedback, and indirectly through usage data. This allows companies to better maintain and optimize their products in the field, and provide high-value input into the design cycle for the next version of the product. It can also provide the raw material for new ideas to create new products and new lines of business.

Revenue Growth, Time-to-Market, and New Lines of Business

We've been discussing predictive maintenance, but the discussion quickly expanded to encompass areas well beyond the traditional role of manufacturing, such is the power of the IoT.

When discussing revenue growth, we tend to think of new products (and this is a definite possibility with a connected factory), but revenue growth comes from a lot of different places. Companies increase their revenue by producing higher-quality products, on time, at lower cost—all things ripe for improvement through connected manufacturing.

Other means are through providing unique services or capabilities. A factory that knows the exact status of every aspect of the line can supply that information, automatically, to customers. Something that used to be a black box, the status of an order, becomes transparent, with the customer knowing exactly where their products are in the line, able to react quickly to changes in schedule, both positive and negative. This is reminiscent of the time when online tracking of packages was first made available by shipping companies.

"Higher quality, lower cost, on-time" is a mantra for manufacturing that is generally achieved by mass producing products. Increasingly, customers are demanding specialized products customized to their needs. Traditionally, this has been handled in a number of ways: human intervention to route products and define settings on the tools, and additional manufacturing lines or even whole factories, each producing a variation of the product, being the most common. These are expensive options that do not scale well with product demand or new customizations.

Connected manufacturers now have the capability to integrate their connected equipment with smart products and the raw materials used to build them. The product being built has a unique identity (e.g., through RFID tagging or bar-coding) and this identity is transmitted to the equipment producing it, allowing the tool to reconfigure itself for that product, and to the routing systems that move the product to the next step in the manufacturing process. The same is true for the components of the product being built—they are tagged, built, and routed to be at the correct station when needed.

The analytics discussed earlier play a crucial role here as the product being built on any given tool is changing frequently. The connections between the tool, the product being built, the quality monitors, and the systems that communicate up and down the supply chain all must be synchronized and react to the unique product being built— a product whose parameters might even change through the manufacturing process.

New lines of business can be created when the connected factory extends it reach. Consider a manufacturer of vacuum cleaners, water systems, air conditioners, or any product that contains filters that must be periodically replaced. If the product has sensors that monitor the filters, the company can automatically detect and replace the filters. This is a new service a company can provide to its customers:

automatic remote monitoring of the state of the filters, with new filters automatically sent to the customer when needed. Analytics plays a big role here as the filter usage and frequency of replacement can be viewed from a wide variety of perspectives: geographic, type (industrial, commercial, home), size, climate, recent weather, type of product, and so on.

It's worth thinking about how this analysis is used. Geography-based analysis leads to changes in stocking levels by geography. Trend analysis determines increases or decreases in manufacturing orders sent to the factory. Multivariate analysis of size, type, and frequency can point to potential upsell opportunities (here again is another revenue growth opportunity).

Usage data from connected products is fed back to the business where it is analyzed for insights that help manufacturing build better products, improve the design of existing products, and create the next generation of products. The latter is key because it is the starting point for an agile company that brings products to market faster than its competitors—the sooner a need is identified, the sooner work can begin, and the more data an enterprise has about how its products are being used, the more informed decisions it can make.

This leads to the realization that connected manufacturing is about more than just building the product. A connected manufacturer has real-time visibility into all aspects of the manufacturing process, including the following:

- Upstream to raw material and component suppliers
- Downstream directly to customers or to the next step in a multi-factory manufacturing process, or to distribution systems
- Orthogonally to research and development, design, even finance

Higher-Quality, Better Products

Connected manufacturers have real-time visibility into quality and compliance data that was the stuff of dreams not so long ago. High-quality manufacturing is mostly about doing the same thing, the same way, every time. We've already discussed how connected manufacturers can use analytics at the edge and the enterprise level to more precisely control the state of the equipment used to manufacture the product. The same can be done for the product itself, whether it's a bicycle, a medication, an integrated circuit, or an automobile.

When we talk about doing "the same thing, the same way, every time," what we really mean is that there is no variation in the manufacturing process. The quality systems are designed and built to create a repeatable process. But there is a gap between creating a sound manufacturing process and executing that process correctly. Understanding this gap, then narrowing, and ultimately eliminating it, is a primary goal of every manufacturer.

Connected manufacturers can now use analytics to understand, to the smallest detail, whether the manufacturing line is actually achieving its goal of no process variance. Let's take for example, an automobile manufacturer that uses robotic welders on its manufacturing line. Every single spot weld can be imaged and stored. These images can be analyzed for deviations from the acceptable output and flagged for additional inspection or rework. Further, this is a perfect application for machine learning systems using image recognition capabilities to completely automate the inspection process.

The next step in quality improvement is to refine the defined process. The same systems used to analyze the gap between desired and actual output for inspection purposes also can be used to understand how best to improve the process. Using our spot-welding example, the systems analyzing the images can be used to zero in on specific problems, find every instance of that problem, and make the data available to quality engineers for root-cause analysis.

Finally, these same systems can be used to run and analyze experiments intended to improve the process. Again, using our spot-welding example, if the factory engineers want to implement a new kind of weld that is thinner (and therefore less expensive) and need to understand whether the weld meets the strength and durability requirements, they can collect all the data using the same systems, join it with the stress test data, and then, using this complete picture, proceed with the development of the new process.

Connected manufacturing can meet the challenge of increased operational efficiency, higher quality and lower cost while simultaneously providing more services in a very agile way. The combination of sensor-equipped tools on the front lines with edge and enterprise analytics providing tactical and strategic direction create

opportunities for dramatic improvements across the entire manufacturing process.

CHAPTER 7

Transforming Health Care

It should go without saying that health care is a priority, and data analysis can help with the many serious challenges associated with this crucial industry.

Demographics and the Need for Connected Health

Maintaining good health and having access to medical care are among the most important things in life. *Access* means both the availability of the appropriate medical care and the ability to afford to pay for it. Collectively, managing health care is a very large problem that consumes lots of resources. Figures 7-1 and 7-2 show how much is spent and the per capita trend of spending on health care.

This is the current state, and the size of the problem will continue to grow. There are four key issues driving the need for dramatic improvements in how we manage health care:

- Our population is aging and we are living longer
- There is a growing shortage of physicians
- We have an increasing need to manage chronic diseases
- Reducing, or at least keeping in check, healthcare costs

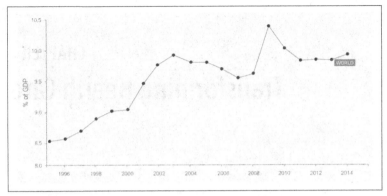

Figure 7-1. Healthcare spending as a percent of GDP[1]

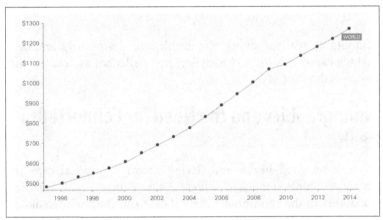

Figure 7-2. Healthcare spending per capita[2]

We review each of these issues, and then discuss how the coming Age of Connected Computing aids in addressing them. However, before we begin, it is important to understand the broad strategic changes the healthcare industry is implementing which act as a framework for these specific solutions. Health care is moving from a fee-for-service model of care to a value-based model.

---

1 Source: World Health Organization Global Health Expenditure database (*http://data.worldbank.org/indicator/SH.XPD.TOTL.ZS*)

2 Source: World Health Organization Global Health Expenditure database (*http://data.worldbank.org/indicator/SH.XPD.PCAP.PP.KD*)

With value-based care, healthcare providers are paid for helping to keep people healthy and for improving the health of those who have chronic conditions. This is done in an evidence-based, cost-effective way. By contrast, the current fee-for-service model pays providers based on the quantity of healthcare services they deliver, such as office visits, tests and procedures. The specific approaches to implement value-based care models are beyond the scope of this discussion, but in general, the focus is shifting away from a healthcare provider–centric view to one centered on the individual patient, whether that patient's needs are preventative, chronic, or acute.

Aging Population

The world's population is aging. Projections show the number of people aged 65 or older will double between 2015 and 2050 (see Figure 7-3).

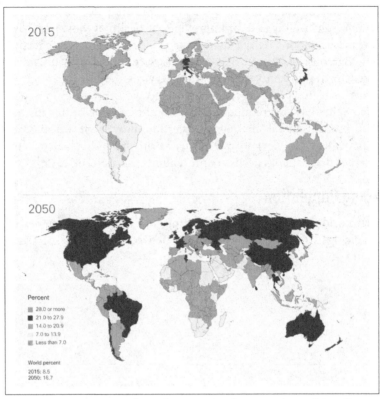

Figure 7-3. Percentage of population 65 and over: 2015 and 2050[3]

This demographic change creates new healthcare challenges that must be addressed.

Physician Shortage

Logically, as the population ages, more healthcare services are needed, and the more services required, the more physicians are needed to administer them. But the problem is more acute because doctors are not interchangeable. There are a large number of specialties in the medical field with more being created each year, so the problem is not just having enough doctors, but having enough of the right kind of doctors. We then need to connect the right doctor

---

3 Source: U.S. Census Bureau, 2013, 2014; International Data Base, U.S. population projections (*http://bit.ly/2v3tNjD*)

with the right patient. In addition, as the population ages and needs more care, so too do the physicians age and retire, thus exacerbating the problem.

We need to educate more doctors and train them more efficiently (including keeping existing doctors informed of new developments in their field). We also need to make more efficient use of physician time, including connecting the right doctor with the right patient (how many times have you gone to the doctor only to be referred to another one—how many healthcare insurance models actually require this?). As we will see, connected computing is poised to dramatically shape the future of doctor/patient interactions.

Chronic Disease

It's no surprise that as the population ages the number of patients with chronic conditions increase. Figure 7-4 shows the rate of that increase. Analytics shows us that an increasing percentage of total healthcare spending is on patients with chronic conditions (>80 percent) as well as the kinds of conditions they have—hypertension, cholesterol, heart disease, and the types of services they use: in-home care, prescriptions, physician visits, in-patient stays, and so on.

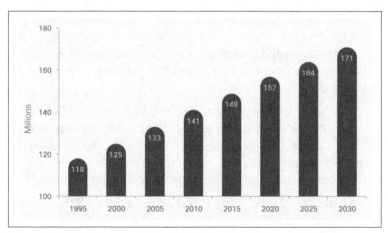

Figure 7-4. Number of people with chronic conditions (in millions)[4]

---

4 Source: Wu, Shin-Yi and Green, Anthony. *Projection of Chronic Illness Prevalence and Cost Inflation* (*http://www.nasuad.org/sites/nasuad/files/hcbs/files/191/9519/ChronicCar eChartbook.pdf*)

Healthcare Costs

The net result of all this is the rising healthcare costs we discussed at the beginning of the section. To address the costs and improve the quality of care, we need to make more effective use of physician time, educate them more efficiently, improve the delivery and quality of medical services, and improve therapies for high-frequency chronic conditions, all with a patient-centric view of the process.

Innovation is already addressing these challenges as we enter the era of connected computing.

Connected Health Care

There are a large number of different activities underway, many of which work in conjunction with one another. The first we'll cover is Electronic Health Records, the core of digitization in health care.

Electronic Health Records

Electronic Health Records, or EHR, is the name given to the drive to create a digital version of the entirety of a patient's medical records. This means not only the local office's records, but all records pertaining to that patient, regardless of the type or location of the healthcare service. Thus, the medical data for the patient from the primary-care physician, specialist physicians, hospital stays, emergency room visits, and prescriptions would all be stored in one place and available to both the patient and any healthcare professionals attending to that patient.

This enables a number of improvements, including making better use of physician's time (as they have all the patient information they need right in front of them); enabling more informed decisions on the part of the physician; and, allowing any physician, anywhere, to quickly come up to speed on the patient's condition and treatment.

It also makes the medical data available to the patient's themselves, increasing patient involvement in the healthcare process; an important need, as the healthcare industry moves toward a more patient-centric process. An additional benefit is a reduction in the risk of negative drug interactions as both the prescribing physician and the pharmacist are aware of all medications the patient is taking.

The EHR is not limited to traditional medical records; it can include data from real-time monitors (e.g., blood pressure or insulin levels) and even the patient's genome. This enables a much more personalized approach to treatment by analyzing the patient's genome, environmental, family history, and social factors, and creating a treatment plan based on that data. It also makes it possible to identify the behaviors, risk factors, and early indicators of disease that enable more effective preventative measures.

Note that security and privacy are key issues that need to be addressed.

Patient-Generated Data

Patient-generated health data (PGHD) is data generated by the patient outside the normal clinical setting. PGHD is taking on a greater role as electronic repositories for health data come online and as the technology for remote monitoring and data collection matures. The larger issues of the aging population, chronic conditions and increasing healthcare costs are also factors.

Wearables and home-based monitoring systems can collect data, often in real time, which can be sent to the healthcare provider to aid in diagnosis as well as evaluation of a treatment's effectiveness. Examples include monitors for blood pressure, heart rate, breathing, glucose levels, oxygen levels, and sleep patterns.

These systems will expand to include local analytics, helping to determine whether the patient needs to take action. They can alert family members or other caregivers of a problem, and, in extreme cases, summon emergency medical help.

Although we tend to think of this as part of a formal healthcare interaction, consumer health devices are increasingly common. These include heart rate and distance monitors for both regular exercise and to help the wearer make improvements towards a healthier lifestyle.

Delivery of Care

Increasingly, doctors and patients are connecting remotely using video, voice, image, and text messaging technology via the internet on home computers, apps on smartphones and tablets, and telepresence robots (the latter prevalent in a hospital setting).

Although this is not a replacement for a physical examination by a trained physician, it is a cost-effective, efficient way to treat simple ailments and handle the large number of routine follow-up appointments that otherwise consume a lot of the patient's and physician's time.

These visits can be supplemented with the aforementioned patient-provided data, and it's easy to see the scope of these kinds of doctor visits increasing as remote monitoring and data collection technology matures. Finally, remote consultation is very convenient for those who are infirm, unable to travel or for whom traveling, even to a local doctor's office, is a burden.

Note that the relative location of the doctor and the patient is completely unimportant. The network eliminates geographical consideration, and this technology greatly enables matching the right doctor with the right patient.

Medication Adherence

Medication adherence, or taking medication as prescribed, is a very big problem. It is a major cause of readmissions, and some estimates put the additional burden of cost on the healthcare system as high as $300 billion. Initial tools to help with this issue were restricted to things like reminder apps on smartphones—useful but reliant on the patient actually taking action when the alarm goes off.

Emerging technology to combat this problem includes IoT-based medication containers that detect when pills are removed from the bottle. The action can be logged with the system triggering an alarm if the pills are not removed when expected. The alert can be sent to more than just the patient: family members, friends, even medical professionals can be recipients who can then follow up.

Going a step further, medication can be formulated with embedded sensors that trigger when the patient swallows a pill (the sensors are the size of a grain of sand and dissolve in the digestive tract). Wearable technology detects the presence of the sensor and logs the action, with similar alert capabilities.

Senior Wellness

Many of the home monitoring, data collection, and remote consultation technologies directly benefit senior wellness and preventive care. They provide for more graceful aging in the home, making seniors more comfortable while simultaneously easing the burden on healthcare facilities. One thing not touched on that applies here is family member involvement. Family members caring for or helping to care for seniors also can attend remote medical consultations, without traveling, and can make use of video technology for remote observation and monitoring of their elder family members.

Machine Learning

The combination of machine learning, big data, increased computational power, and new techniques in training neural networks is finally producing real, useful results in artificial intelligence. Machine learning applied to large datasets allows clinicians to create more effective treatments. The increase in data being collected (including the aforementioned patient-provided data) creates new opportunities to analyze the efficacy of a treatment across a much broader set of variables.

Machine learning now exceeds human abilities in image recognition so tasks like analyzing x-rays can be off-loaded to computers. Even more, the entire library of images can be accessed and analyzed systematically to identify commonalities—something that simply isn't possible for humans.

Many common ailments lend themselves well to diagnosis by an Artificial Intelligence (AI) system. This is already being done for both common and uncommon diseases, though it is in the early stages. This is particularly interesting when you add in the global context: consider that the AI system will have access to the larger community and be aware of other diagnoses being made (rigorously quantifying subjective statements like "the flu is going around"). This facilitates both more accurate diagnoses and early warning for outbreaks and epidemics.

As with remote visits, the data from wearables, biosensors, and home monitoring greatly expand the possibilities when joined with machine learning diagnostic systems.

It is not difficult to envision a time when all healthcare diagnostic services begin remotely using an IoT-based medical diagnostic kit that is connected to an artificial intelligence diagnostic system. The diagnostic kit takes routine measurements like temperature, blood pressure, oxygen levels, basic blood tests, and so on and sends it to the diagnostic system. The patient interacts with the AI via video, audio, text, and imaging systems, and the AI combines the diagnostic data and the symptoms with the patient's medical history (from the EHR) and makes a diagnosis.

At a minimum, an enormous amount of routine work is offloaded from the healthcare system. Taking it one step further the AI system can recommend a prescription, submit both the prescription and the data supporting the request to the pharmacy and have the prescription automatically filled.

CHAPTER 8

Connected Transportation

Cars are one of the most popular modes of transportation for a significant portion of the world's population. With their popularity has come a host of problems, not the least of which are pollution, traffic jams, and a dramatic increase in the number of accidental deaths. We are in the early stages of two dramatic evolutions in the automobile: autonomous driving and connected vehicles.

Autonomous Driving

We'll begin our discussion with autonomous driving. The global automotive market is so large and the technology so revolutionary that the landscape will be very different after it has become an accepted technology seeing wide use.

Additionally, it's important to make a distinction between "connected cars" and "intelligent cars." A *connected car* is a digitized vehicle with built-in wireless networking enabling advanced information and entertainment systems, app integration, real-time location and routing services, vehicle-to-vehicle and vehicle-to-infrastructure communication systems, and remote diagnostic and update systems. These cars are loaded with sensors generating on the order of 25 GB of data every hour. An *intelligent car* builds on the connected car with additional sensors and computing systems enabling the car to drive without human direction.

Self-driving cars have been a staple of science fiction for decades, but it is only recently that advances in sensor technology, computer hardware, and machine learning software techniques have made it feasible. Google's self-driving car initiative and Tesla's lane-keeping system are two high-profile examples, but they are merely the tip of the iceberg as virtually every major car manufacturer is working on, and has formal plans to introduce autonomous vehicle technology in the near future.

Here's a quick review of the various levels of autonomy:

Level one
Relatively minor driver assisted technology like cruise control, stop-and-go automation in low-speed traffic jams, or automated parallel parking.

Level two
Partial automation in which the human driver is in charge, but some elements, like steering, acceleration, and braking are controlled by the computer.

Level three
More sophisticated, with the primary differentiator being that the vehicle has sensors it uses to understand the environment. An example is Tesla's system for highway lane-keeping at high speed. This could also include lane changing with blind spot technology.

Level four
Complete self-driving by the computers but the human driver is expected to be alert and ready to take over if intervention is needed. This is the level many car manufacturers are aiming for within the next five years.

Level five
Full automation. No human direction or intervention is required. In fact, steering wheels, gear shifts, and accelerator and braking pedals aren't needed. This is the level Google's Waymo is targeting.

Some people struggle to accept that full automation is possible. Ten years ago, it wasn't; but now, Google's self-driving cars have more than three million miles of real-world driving experience. The data from those miles has been used for more than one billion miles of simulation. These simulations are used to test and refine the self-driving system, which then is applied to real-world driving tests, the results of which are fed back to further improve the system. Tesla has 300 million miles driven using its Autopilot system and more than one billion miles of real-world sensor data. BMW is aggressively pursuing development of autonomous driving. It intends to put a fleet of 40 autonomous test vehicles on the roads in 2017; and while most automobile manufacturers have plans for level three or level four autonomy in the next five years, BMW is aiming for full level five autonomy by the year 2021.

This is the power of the connected world. Each individual, be it a car, a person, or an isolated sensor, contributes their data, collectively enabling a greater understanding of the whole. Let's now look at the follow-on effects of autonomous vehicle technology, many of which represent opportunities to apply analytics to data to improve customer experiences and create completely new lines of business.

Collaborative Consumption

Motor vehicles as an asset class are horribly underused. There are more than one billion cars on the road with a utilization rate of less than five percent! Ninety-five percent of the time cars are sitting idle. The reasons are obvious: cars need drivers who are otherwise engaged as soon as they arrive at their destination; and drivers need cars available at specific times when they need to travel.

Self-driving vehicles radically alter this dynamic. When no driver is required, the car is available for use elsewhere; and when the "driver" needs transportation, the car can be summoned to pick them up. Thus, fully autonomous vehicles can be shared, and the number of ways they can be shared is limited only by the imagination.

A family can share a single car, taking the children to and from school and the parents to and from work, even when schedules are very different:

1. The children are dropped off at (multiple) schools
2. The car drives itself back home taking the parents to (multiple) workplaces
3. The car drives itself to a shop for scheduled maintenance
4. Next, it drives back to pick up the children at the end of the school day, taking them home

5. Finally, it drives itself to the parents' workplace to take them home

A similar number of total miles are being driven but it's being done with only one vehicle instead of two, three, or four. The cost savings are compelling.

For that matter, multiple families can share a single vehicle in the same way, and taking it a step further, neighborhoods can have shared-use vehicles available for checkout. Companies can supply self-driving commute vehicles for their employees to schedule and use. Colleges can do the same for students.

The same vehicle can be made available for use to others as part of an Uber-like ride hailing system, thus turning a previously unused asset into a source of revenue that offsets the cost of the vehicle.

It's easy to envision private companies being created to provide transportation services made up of fleets of self-driving cars, completely eliminating the need for individual vehicle ownership. Analytics will play a big role here as understanding where, how, and when vehicles are in demand is key to success, particularly as the way in which cars are used evolves as the possibilities become manifest.

Types of Autonomous Vehicles

Another factor to consider is the type of vehicle. Currently, cars are designed specifically to accommodate the needs of a human driver. Completely autonomous vehicles do not have these requirements and the interior space of the car can be reimagined to serve any number of common or custom uses.

The interior of the car can be converted into an office, complete with all the amenities in a traditional office: desk, computer, network connections, printer, coffee maker, and so forth. By extension, this includes full WebEx and Telepresence capabilities for meeting with colleagues, partners, and customers. Time spent commuting will no longer be wasted time, but can instead be put to productive use; not to mention how useful it will be for jobs with lots of travel involved.

Cars do not need to be the size they are now. When vehicle-to-vehicle communication is standardized and implemented, vehicles can be designed to suit their purpose rather than being big enough to be seen by a human driver. They can be designed to very efficiently carry only a single person. Or not be intended to carry human passengers at all, perhaps as a delivery vehicle from the local store, meal delivery (think pizza), or fleets of very small cars used to deliver packages.

Second-Order Effects

Fatalities from automobile accidents have been steadily dropping for 25 years. However, there are still more than five million accidents every year in the United States alone, with more than 30,000 fatalities and millions of serious injuries. Estimates range from 30 to 50 percent of the fatalities are caused by drunk driving.

Autonomous vehicles do not drink; they don't grow tired; they are not distracted by smart phones or other passengers; and they don't fall asleep. They do obey all traffic laws, can sense their surroundings in all directions continuously and are programmed with safety as the highest priority. Traffic accidents, fatalities and injuries will drop in direct relation to the number of self-driving cars on the road. They will become so rare that a traffic fatality will make the news as a headline item.

With reduced traffic accidents comes a reduced number of serious injuries. There are literally millions of injuries every year caused by accidents that require medical consultation. These injuries will disappear over time alleviating pressure on the healthcare system. We will also need fewer body shops.

With self-driving cars, traffic tickets become a thing of the past. That means fewer traffic police are needed as well as freeing up judges and judicial infrastructure currently completely dedicated to traffic tickets.

Internet of Things for Cars

A connected car is a digitized vehicle with built-in wireless networking enabling advanced information and entertainment systems, app integration, real-time location and routing services, vehicle-to-vehicle and vehicle-to-infrastructure communication systems, and remote diagnostic and update systems.

Connected vehicles have both the network connections of the home or office and the sensor technology of a factory. In fact, these vehicles are loaded with sensors generating on the order of 25 GB of data every hour.

There are dramatic benefits for the car manufacturer. Updates to the onboard computer systems can be made wirelessly without requiring a visit to the dealer. This is especially important in cases for which safety is involved. Notifications of recalls can be made directly in the vehicle instead of the current postal mail method that is fraught with opportunity for missed communication.

With sensors collecting data on everything from speed, acceleration, and braking efficiency to fuel consumption and power-to-drivetrain ratios, manufacturers can harness enormous amounts of data to help them improve their designs.

Further, analytics applied to this data can be used to improve the performance of the vehicle in real time. Manufacturers can take all of the data for that model car and analyze it to understand what are the optimal ranges of values for various operating parameters. This information can be transmitted to the vehicle's onboard systems at periodic intervals becoming the baseline against which to compare actual operating performance. If something is outside the defined range, the vehicle's systems can make adjustments to produce optimal performance.

Note the edge- and enterprise-level analytics happening here. The edge devices (the vehicles) are providing their individual data on performance to the enterprise systems. This data is analyzed in aggregate to determine best-case operating ranges. Those ranges are transmitted to the vehicle. The vehicle's systems (the edge device) are analyzing performance in real time against enterprise-supplied ranges and making adjustments as need, again in real time.

The same data can be used to identify issues and bring them to the attention of the driver. Examples include tire pressure, brake-pad life, fluid levels and quality—if it can be measured, it can be used. In the same way that factories make use of data for predictive maintenance, vehicle systems can use the data being generated to identify when maintenance is needed in a far more sophisticated way than the current fixed schedule.

Connected cars have the potential to transform the driving experience. Remote start systems can start the car and adjust the climate control to comfortable levels before the owner even opens the door. Integrated wireless networks bring all the connectivity of the home or office to the car. Built-in navigation systems are just the beginning. In the same way that there are apps for smart phones there will be apps for cars: programs specifically designed to enhance the car driving and passenger riding experience.

For example, an analytics app running in the car can look at the fuel level, average mileage per gallon, and the destination to determine if or when fuel will be needed. But it can go a step further by using geolocation services, online pricing information, and reviews to suggest a gas station where you might want to stop.

Entertainment systems can be directly integrated into a connected vehicle. Access to music sites like Spotify or Pandora are obvious choices. Games and video, as well, although these need to be restricted to the back seat at the moment to avoid distracting the driver. This issue will disappear as soon as level five autonomous vehicles are available. At that point, the interior of the car can be converted into an entertainment center.

Finally, connected vehicle technology allows the owner to remotely monitor the vehicle's health, location, fuel consumption, speed, and driving behavior. This has obvious benefits for industries with fleets of vehicles but is useful even closer to home as teenagers begin to drive.

Public Transportation

Bringing connected technology to public transportation has immediate benefits for all travelers. Real-time transit data, where the bus or train is now and when it will arrive, as well as when is the next bus or train if I miss that one, is invaluable for people as they make their way through the day.

Similarly, moving payment capabilities to the smartphone makes the use of the mass transit system far more convenient. Data provided by a connected transit system enables analytics that help the transit authority to understand demand for routes strategically for route definition and tactically for real-time adjustments.

Uber-like solutions for public transportation become possible, making public transport more flexible. Autonomous driving technology has the potential to completely transform large parts of public transit. For example, instead of a large bus on a fixed schedule, picture many smaller, autonomously driven, zero-emission vehicles responding to individual requests along defined but flexible routes.

Finally, in-vehicle advertising—that is, displaying ads to passengers. In some ways, this could transform public transit more than anything else. If the same kind of analytics-driven targeted advertising used on websites is applied to the much more captive audience of an Uber-like public transit vehicle, a new revenue stream is created, one that could entice private companies to enter the market, alleviating the government of the burden.

Insurance

Connected vehicle technology brings challenges and opportunities to the insurance industry. Connected vehicles can continuously collect data on how the vehicle is being operated. This data makes possible insurance based on the actual usage of the vehicle. Usage-based insurance breaks down into combinations of the following categories:

Pay as you drive
Insurance premiums are calculated based on the actual number of miles driven.

Pay where you drive
Certain areas have more accidents than others (e.g., urban versus rural driving), so insurance companies can offer different rates based on where the vehicle is actually driven.

Pay based on how you drive
Data from the vehicle is analyzed to determine how good a driver you are. The factors that can be analyzed are very broad: how many times the speed limit is exceeded; number of right turns that fail to come to a complete stop; excessive acceleration; number of times abrupt braking is used; number of times the car swerves abruptly.

And here is a good example of an app that meshes perfectly with this new reality: the Good Driver app. This app would monitor, in real time, the aforementioned driving behaviors, providing feedback to the driver to be used to improve his driving. The app helps drivers keep their usage-based insurance rates low. It also can be used for fleet management and for parents to monitor the driving behavior of their children.

Pay based on how much autonomous driving you use
Finally, as autonomous driving becomes more commonplace, and proves to be safer, insurance companies will offer different rates when autonomous driving is used versus manual control.

Note that from the data processing perspective, these are nontrivial exercises. It's a lot of data for a lot of cars. There are edge-level analytics that need to be run on each vehicle in order to calculate rates, and there are aggregate enterprise-level analytics for the insurance companies to use to understand how to set rates.

There is opportunity here for insurance companies to use analytics to differentiate themselves from their competitors by providing better rates with a more informed understanding of their risk.

Fleet Management

Many of the same kinds of applications of data from connected cars we've been discussing can be used to significantly improve the management of both small and large fleets of vehicles.

Location management (knowing precisely where everyone is) takes on new dimensions and adds a level of flexibility to changes in scheduling that are difficult and time consuming to do manually.

Data coming in from all vehicles in the fleet allows the fleet manager, using a sophisticated analytics engine, to optimize routes, ensuring that drivers are traveling to their destination in the most efficient way. This same level of communication enables real-time alerts to be posted throughout the fleet network. Notifications for traffic accidents, road construction, road conditions like icy patches, and weather conditions enable route adjustments that improve efficiency and reduce cost.

Tools to manage driver performance become available like those discussed in the Insurance section. These analytics also enable gamification of driver behavior by providing incentives and rewards for good behavior related to safety, efficiency, cost, and vehicle maintenance.

Vehicle performance can be managed in a much more data-driven way, and this analysis can be used to aid in making purchase decisions for new additions to the fleet.

Lastly, proactive and predictive maintenance analytics are just as valuable in this instance as they are in the manufacturing industry. Using data to change from a fixed maintenance schedule to an adaptive one lowers routine maintenance costs, avoids expensive breakdowns, and keeps the fleet running efficiently.

Conclusion

We are currently in the midst of a digital transformation brought about by the combination of ubiquitous low-cost computing power, the global internet, and advanced data processing techniques. As the number of connections to the global network increases, and as the amount of data they produce explodes, the Age of Connected Computing is born.

Harnessing the data through analytics is mandatory in order stay competitive, and in many cases, in order to stay relevant. Remember, only 12 percent of the Fortune 500 companies from 1955 still exist today; the rest did not survive the creative destruction brought about by the steady march of technological innovation.

The current technology disruption is not a one-time event. Change is continuous, and, in fact, the rate of change is speeding up—the time between disruptions is lessening. Each disruption brings about change, which then becomes the standard, embraced by all, and lays the foundation for the next innovative leap.

Today, harnessing the power of enormous volumes of data through analytics must be mastered in order to stay competitive. Those who turn data into insight through analytics will create new products, new services and improved customer experiences. The investment in time and resources is well worth it, both today and into the future as we journey towards the next disruption.

About the Author

Raghunath Nambiar is the chief technology officer of Cisco's Unified Computing System (UCS) business. He helps define strategies for next generation architectures, systems, and datacenter solutions, as well as leading a team of engineers and product leaders focused on emerging technologies and solutions. He has played an instrumental role in accelerating the growth of the Cisco UCS to a top datacenter compute platform. Raghu was previously a Cisco distinguished engineer and chief architect of big data and analytics solution engineering, responsible for incubating and growing it to a mainstream portfolio. He brings years of technical accomplishments with significant expertise in systems architecture, performance engineering, and creating disruptive technologies and solutions.

Raghu has served on several industry standard committees for performance evaluation, and program committees of leading academic and research conferences. He chaired industry's first standards committee for benchmarking big data systems and is presently the chair of the standards committee for benchmarking Internet of Things (IoT). He has published more than 50 peer-reviewed papers and book chapters, and holds six patents with several pending.

Prior to Cisco, Raghu was an architect at Hewlett-Packard responsible for several industry-first and disruptive technologies and solutions and a decade of performance benchmark leadership. Raghu holds master's degrees from University of Massachusetts and Goa University, and completed an advanced management program from Stanford University.

CPSIA information can be obtained
at www.ICGtesting.com
Printed in the USA
FSOW03n1525230917